Folens

Essentia

EastEnders Scripts

Models for Writing

Selected by Mike Gould

© 2003 Folens Limited, on behalf of the authors.

UK: Folens Publishers, Apex Business Centre, Boscombe Road, Dunstable, LU5 4RL.
Email: folens@folens.com

Ireland: Folens Publishers, Greenhills Road, Tallaght, Dublin 24.
Email: info@folens.ie

Poland: JUKA, ul. Renesansowa 38, Warsaw 01-905.

Editor: Emma Thomas
Layout artist: Suzanne Ward
Cover design: Duncan McTeer
Cover image: BBC Picture Archives
First published 2003 by Folens Limited.

Every effort has been made to contact copyright holders of material used in this publication.
If any copyright holder has been overlooked, we should be pleased to make any necessary
arrangements.

British Library Cataloguing in Publication Data. A catalogue record for this publication is
available from the British Library.

ISBN 1-84303-444-1

Folens gratefully acknowledges the support of John Yorke, who made the original selection of texts; the EastEnders team; and the BBC Drama Series Department.

Acknowledgements

Text extracts:

Episode 194 by Tony Holland. Reproduced by permission of the author and the author's agent PFD.

Episode 248 by Charlie Humphreys. Reproduced by permission of Cecily Ware Literary Agents on behalf of the Estate of Charlie Humphreys.

Episode 401 by Tony McHale. Reproduced by permission of Cecily Ware Literary Agents on behalf of the author.

Episode 479 by Tony Jordan. Reproduced by permission of Bill McLean Personal Management on behalf of the author.

Episode 756 by Simon Ashdown. Reproduced by permission of The Agency, London, on behalf of the author.

Episode 34 by Tony Jordan. Reproduced by permission of Bill McLean Personal Management on behalf of the author.

Photographs:
Cover image: BBC Picture Archives; page 8: BBC Picture Archives; page 19: BBC Picture Archives; page 26: BBC Picture Archives; page 33: BBC Picture Archives; page 47: BBC Picture Archives; page 58: BBC Picture Archives; page 69: BBC Picture Archives; page 77: BBC Picture Archives; page 81: BBC Picture Archives; page 95: BBC Picture Archives.

Contents

Introduction   **5**

Your questions answered   **6**

1: Den and Angie: Christmas Day   **7**

Episode 194 by Tony Holland   9

2: Dot and Ethel: East End Memories   **17**

Episode 248 by Charlie Humphreys   19

3: Cindy leaves the Square   **31**

Episode 401 by Tony McHale   33

4: Ricky and Bianca's Wedding Morning   **45**

Episode 479 by Tony Jordan   47

5: Tiffany and Grant: Tug-of-love   **67**

Episode 756 by Simon Ashdown   69

6: Kat and Zoe: Mother and Child   **79**

Episode 34 by Tony Jordan   81

Introduction

Essential EastEnders Scripts

Why should I be interested in *EastEnders* scripts?

Even if you are not one of the 16 million people who watch *EastEnders* every week, there are many good reasons to read the scripts. First and foremost, they tell great stories with great characters.

I can understand that, but if I want great stories and characters, I can watch the programme: why study them in school or college?

The simple reason is that they provide great models of how to write drama. Writing drama, particularly for a specific form – the thirty-minute soap – is a real skill, and is much, much more than writing a few scenes and throwing in the odd shock or revelation. Writing in this way is very focused and sharp – and requires real talent.

Is reading and writing drama important for exams?

Of course. All the assessments you face in school in English will have an assessment of drama of one sort or another, whether it is Shakespeare in the Key Stage 3 tests and GCSE, or drama texts in GCSE English Literature.

But surely if I need to read good drama, I should be reading Shakespeare?

Absolutely. But these *EastEnders* scripts are perhaps the closest thing we have to modern-day Shakespeare plays. They may not have the same depth of language but they use different, modern conventions to make stunning drama – note the simple use of scene directions, the simple images used to convey a character's emotions and the powerful dialogue.

A lot of what I do isn't drama scripts, though.

That's true, but as you will see from these scripts, the range of writing skills required transfers across all genres; for example, you still have to tell good stories in prose, and use sparkling description. The skills you learn here will help your writing generally, and help improve exam and assessment grades.

OK, you've convinced me. But what's so essential about these particular scripts?

These scripts were originally selected by John Yorke, former Executive Producer of *EastEnders*, as examples of some of the best, and most famous, episodes. They cover a wide range – from the death of a major character, to the marriage of two more. From the escape of a key character from the Square, to the memories of two of the stalwarts of the series. They also cover a range of forms – two-handers (with only two actors involved) to ensemble playing (with practically the whole cast on screen).

So, I want to improve my grades and become a top-class writer. How do I do it?

First of all, read this book, and look at the key features we have pointed out! They draw your attention to some of the key language features in scripts, and in writing generally. After that, it's up to you!

Introduction by John Yorke

(Head of BBC Drama Series and Executive Producer of *EastEnders* from January 2000 to May 2002)

One of the reasons *EastEnders* has been successful over the years is that the writers and producers have always considered it to be serious drama. Charles Dickens was dismissed in his lifetime; Alfred Hitchcock too, simply because they were very popular. But being popular doesn't mean being bad. Whether it's Shakespeare or a soap, it's all storytelling; and whatever their form, we all crave good stories, and – as I hope this collection shows – there have been some great stories in *EastEnders* – and great characters.

But what makes a good soap story? There are a number of basic principles: firstly, stories should always emerge from character and not vice versa, and secondly – it's best to keep things small. Soaps always seem to come unstuck when they deal with the extraordinary rather than the everyday: sieges, kidnaps, mystery killer viruses all tend to stretch the audience's credulity if they're used on a regular basis. The most successful stories (and we have admittedly had the odd kidnap ourselves!) tend to be small in scale, although obviously big to the characters concerned. This in turn underlines the importance of empathy.

Emotional identification with the characters is vital. The audience has to love the characters; though this doesn't necessarily mean these characters have to be nice. Over the years audiences have loved EastEnders baddies, from Den Watts, through David Wicks to Grant Mitchell and Alfie Moon, largely because whatever their sins, they always had something about them that made them redeemable. The reason they've worked is not because they're bad, but ironically because they were also capable of good. Den's love for Sharon and David's for Bianca always stopped them being two-dimensional villains.

The writers, of course, are at the heart of this success, but the scripts aren't just written on a whim. There is a long-term planning conference four times a year in which a central team of writers review all the characters and discuss possible story arcs. This is followed by a regular monthly conference in which the same writers plot out the events in each chosen story into episodes, until it's felt that there is enough material for each programme to be a) funny b) sad c) fast moving, and give people something to talk about the next day. These episode outlines are then given to writers whose job it is to turn them into finished episodes – a process which can take between two and ten drafts. This is a useful thing for young writers to know – writing isn't easy, and redrafting is a natural, and necessary, part of the process.

The scripts in this book come from classic episodes of *EastEnders*; episodes when the key elements – acting, writing, storyline, character and direction all came together. These episodes tend to be culminations of long-running storylines. *EastEnders* works by building towards occasional 'explosions' (i.e. key moments of high drama or revelation), raking over the aftermath and then building slowly towards another explosion again. The explosions tend to be what viewers remember; although there are lots of smaller episodes that have moments of which the writer can feel equally proud.

If you want to be the next Tony Jordan – or indeed the next Charles Dickens or J.K. Rowling, there is only one thing you must do. Write. Writing isn't easy, and almost nobody is able to write well for the programme when they start. It takes a great deal of practice and patience, and a huge amount of soul-searching and insecurity to boot. This is probably true of all writing, but especially true of writing for television. Unless you have the drive, the stamina, and also the self-belief you're going to find it very hard – it's a very bruising profession. Most of all though, you absolutely have to love the show you're writing for. If you approach it like a piece of hack work, it's going to look like a piece of hack work. The scripts here show that the writers treated the show seriously and wanted to make a mark on their audiences. I think they succeeded. Now read the scripts, and see if you agree.

1

Den and Angie: Christmas Day

Writer: Tony Holland

Transmission date: 25 December 1986

revelation and revenge

About the text

Type: Ensemble acting

This classic early episode from 1986 features Den, the landlord of the Queen Vic pub and his wife, Angie. Drama series, especially soaps, tend to build towards key dramatic events or moments through the year, so it is no surprise that this major scene is set on Christmas Day. It is helpful to know that Angie invented the fact that she has six months to live in order to keep her womanising husband. The text is an ideal example of 'ensemble' acting – in which a group interacts yet within it there are individual dialogues and dramas.

This script is by Tony Holland, who created the series with it its first producer, Julia Smith.

Word level

- Clearly there is a good deal of idiom (informal language) in this script, as in other extracts. Think about the use of 'CARVED UP' on page 10. Why is this choice of phrase especially appropriate?

Sentence level

- As in many scripts in which writers are imitating speech, there are many abbreviated or incomplete sentences. How would the script be affected if these were written as full sentences?

Text level

- All drama depends on dramatic irony – when one character or more knows about something that has happened, or is going to happen, but no one else does. Can you find any examples of this in this episode?

- How does the writer draw a contrast between the characters and behaviour of Den and Angie on page 11?

- The last line of the episode is like a punchline. Why is it so effective?

Episode 194
by Tony Holland

Main Characters

Dennis Watts – landlord of the Queen Vic
Angie Watts – his wife
Sharon Watts – their adoptive daughter

Pete Beale – Pauline Fowler's twin brother, the original fruit and veg trader
Kathy Beale – Pete's second wife
Ian Beale – their son
Lou Beale – Pete and Pauline's mother

Arthur Fowler – redundant toy factory worker, allotment keeper
Pauline Fowler – his wife, launderette assistant
Michelle Fowler – their daughter

'Lofty' Holloway – barman at the Queen Vic (real name George)

Pat Wicks – Pete Beale's first wife, later Pat Butcher, now known as Pat Evans
Simon Wicks – her son, 'Wicksy'

Ali Osman – original owner of the café
Sue Osman – his wife

Dot Cotton – chain-smoking launderette assistant
Ethel Skinner – Dot's oldest friend

Tom – Sharon's friend
Mary Smith – chaotic single mum
Wilmott-Brown – owner of The Dagmar
Debbie Wilkins – former barmaid at the Queen Vic

SCENE: 27. INT. PUB DOWNSTAIRS. DAY. [3.15pm]

[THE BIG EAT IS OVER. KATHY STARTS TO CLEAR UP]

ANGIE: No – leave it girl. Sit down. Let yourself catch your breath. Here, look at the little'n, miles away. Pat'll be spark out soon. [INDICATING ETHEL] Look at her ... I could do with a nap miself ... I'm **whacked**.

KATHY: Well – it's a big thing to take on. Dinner for us lot.

[THEY'RE BOTH DRINKING]

ANGIE: But I wanted to. I sort of needed to. Had to. Fancied having all me mates round me ... [BEAT] Mind you. I slipped up a bit with Pat. I'm sorry about that. Still you did enjoy yourself?

KATHY: 'Course.

ANGIE: So did I ... [cont]

[ANGIE LOOKS ACROSS TO THE OTHER SIDE OF THE PUB, WHERE DEN AND PETE ARE TALKING.

SHE WISHES DEN COULD HEAR HER – SO HE'S REMINDED SHE'S ONLY SUPPOSED TO HAVE SIX MONTHS TO LIVE]

ANGIE: [cont] D'you know what's the best Christmas present? Me and him still being together. There was a time you know, in the not too distant past, when I nearly lost him ... Cos he was worried about me ...

[KATHY, KNOWING THE FULL STORY, AND THAT ANGIE IS GOING TO GET 'CARVED UP' BY DEN AT CHRISTMAS, IS EMBARRASSED, REMAINS QUIET.]

DEN GOES BEHIND THE BAR TO GET A REFILL FOR HIMSELF AND PETE.

ANGIE IS AWARE HE'S THERE, INCREASES THE VOLUME OF HER VOICE]

ANGIE: Worried about the state of me health ... he cared ... he loved me enough to stay ...

KATHY: You're alright though, Ange. Sound as a bell, you.

ANGIE: Am I ...?

[SOME ANCIENT ROCK-N-ROLL NUMBER]

Music: "They Call It Rock 'n' Roll" by Delaney & Bonnie & Friends

DEN: Come on, Ange. Remember this? Come on.

[AND HE COMES ROUND THE BAR, TAKES HER HAND AND STARTS TO JIVE WITH HER, THEY DO IT RATHER WELL.

PETE AND KATHY LOOK ON

ETHEL WAKES UP.

SHARON AND TOM ARRIVE FROM UPSTAIRS.

SEE ANGIE'S FACE - ALL HAPPINESS.

SEE DEN'S - AS HARD AS NAILS]

SCENE: 28. INT. LOU'S DOWNSTAIRS. DAY. [3.30pm]

STUDIO

TV: Sound "The Railway Children"

    [POST DINNER.

    PAULINE STANDS IN THE KITCHEN DOORWAY.

    DOT IS ASLEEP.

    IAN AND WICKSY ARE WATCHING THE MOVIE ON THE TELLY.

    PAULINE LOOKS AT THEM ALL THEN GOES INTO THE KITCHEN CLOSING THE DOOR BEHIND HER.

    ARTHUR IS WASHING UP. HIS FACE IS SET AS HARD AS DEN'S]

PAULINE: Arthur, I know it was all an act.

    [SHE TOUCHES HIS ARM BUT HE SHRUGS IT AWAY]

But thanks ever so much for coming down. I did appreciate it.

ARTHUR: Well ... I can't have everyone's day ruined cos of one person ...

    [PAULINE LOOKS AT THE REMAINS OF THE CHICKEN]

PAULINE: There won't be any chicken sandwiches in the house on Boxing Day, will there?

    [ARTHUR LOOKS AT THE CARCASS, AND WE SEE IT]

ARTHUR: ... It looks like I feel ...

PAULINE: [CHANGING THE SUBJECT] Oh Arthur won't you change your mind and come over to the pub tonight for a drink, eh?

BEAT long pause
STEAMED-UP drunk
Lady Muck haughty woman who likes to be waited on

ARTHUR: No. I'll look after the kids. You go ...
[**BEAT**] and please — let me do this on me own. I can
manage best on me own.

[AND, RATHER SADLY, PAULINE GOES INTO THE OTHER
ROOM.

ARTHUR CONTINUES TO WASH UP, THEN HE STOPS: DEAD.
HE STARES INTO THE WASHING UP WATER]

SCENE: 30. INT. PUB DOWNSTAIRS. NIGHT. [7.55pm]

Music: "Is This Love?" by Alison Moyet

[IF POSSIBLE, START ON THE DOOR OF THE GENTS
WITH A BIG NOTICE ON IT: CLOSED FOR REPAIRS.
SORRY GENTS!

JUST ABOUT EVERYONE'S THERE.

DEN AND ANGIE SERVING BEHIND THE BAR, ANGIE FAIRLY
STEAMED-UP BY NOW.

LOFTY, WICKSY, ETHEL, MICHELLE, PAT, PETE, KATHY,
SUE, ALI, TOM, DEBS, WILMOTT-BROWN, MARY, PAULINE.

TONY, HANNAH, KELVIN, CARMEL AND CASSIE MAKE THEIR
ENTRANCE AT THE TOP OF THE SCENE.

START WITH DEBS, WILMOTT-BROWN AND PAT]

DEBS: No — he did the cooking. I just sat there like
Lady Muck. Pouring the drinks. Changing the records ...

PAT: [TO WILMOTT-BROWN] Good cook are you?

WILMOTT-BROWN: Pretty fair.

PAT: Just like you.

WILMOTT-BROWN: Sorry?

PAT: Pretty and fair.

    [PAT IS NOT VERY SOBER.

    GO TO MICHELLE, LOFTY AND PAULINE]

MICHELLE: So he don't mind looking after Vicki?

PAULINE: No, 'course not. So – it was a great success then?

LOFTY: You should have seen it. The best Christmas I've ever had ...

    [GO TO DOT, SUE AND ALI. ALI HAS A WHISTLING KEY-RING]

DOT: I got one for Colin.

ALI: Dad gave it to me.

DOT: Is that where you had your lunch?

SUE: Every year.

DOT: 'Course you don't celebrate Christmas, do you?

ALI: No but any excuse for a party.

    [GO TO WICKSY, ETHEL, TOM AND MARY.

    WICKSY COLLECTING GLASSES OUT OF THE GOODNESS OF HIS HEART]

WICKSY: [TO ETHEL] Alright Et? [TO MARY] You smell nice.

MARY: Present from your mum.

[WICKSY DOESN'T WISH TO KNOW THAT AND PUTS THE GLASSES ON THE BAR]

TOM: Excuse me, ladies.

   [HE MOVES OFF.

   GO TO PETE AND KATHY]

KATHY: He wouldn't dare do it. Not on Christmas Day.

PETE: I hope you're right.

   [DEN ARRIVES AT THE BAR - LOOKS OVER AT ANGIE]

DEN: [TO PETE AND KATHY] Gone to her head a bit fast. Comes of being on the wagon for so long.

KATHY: She's alright. Having a good time, that's all.

DEN: Needs to lie down. D'you mind taking over for a bit?

KATHY: 'Course not. Simon! Come and give us a hand ...

DEN: [TO ANGIE] Angie, can we have a word?

   [AS HE LEADS HER TO THE BACK CORRIDOR, SO WICKSY AND KATHY TAKE OVER SERVING.

   OMINOUS LOOK BETWEEN PETE AND KATHY.

   WE GO WITH DEN AND ANGIE]

DEN: How d'you feel?

ANGIE: How do I feel. I'm **bushed**. Well it's been a hell of a day ain't it? And I ain't very strong am I? [cont]

   [ARMS AROUND HIM]

ANGIE: [cont] Thanks for the best Christmas ever Den.

DEN: Our last one ...

ANGIE: Yeah. You don't regret staying with me, do you? Don't answer that! I don't want to get all morbid, today of all days ... But it scares me. I don't think I can keep up this performance twenty-four hours a day.

    [HE REMOVES HER ARMS FROM HIM]

DEN: You could keep this performance up for a lifetime.

    [SOMETHING IN THE TONE OF HIS VOICE FRIGHTENS HER]

DEN: Like on the Orient Express. Like in the bar. Like chatting up that barman. "I've told my husband this terrible lie" ... "not a white one but a big black one ...." Remember Ange, 'cos I do, I was sitting four feet away from you - lapping up every word ... Six little months to live ... six tragic little months ... and poor old Angie is going to pop off.

[SERIOUS] That is the sickest joke you have ever played. And Dennis Watts fell for it. Now the joke's on you ...

    [HE PRODUCES THE LETTER FROM HIS POCKET]

This, my sweet, is a letter from my solicitor. In a nutshell it tells you that your husband has filed a petition for divorce. And it also tells you to get yourself a solicitor pretty damn quick.

    [SHE'S SO STUNNED THAT SHE DOESN'T TAKE THE LETTER.

    SO HE FORCES IT INTO HER HAND]

Happy Christmas, Angie.

    [AND HE LEAVES HER STANDING THERE]

2

Dot and Ethel: East End Memories

Writer: Charlie Humphreys

Transmission date: 2 July 1987

memories and friendship

About the text

Type: Two-hander

This extract from an episode in 1987, written by Charlie Humphreys, bears comparison with great drama written by writers such as Alan Bennett and Harold Pinter. It has humour, drama and raw emotion, and is a marvellous example of a 'two-hander', that's to say, drama for two actors. This section features old friends, Dot and Ethel. Dot is a devout Christian. Ethel is rather different! Both have suffered in their own ways. In this extract, they are looking after Michelle Fowler's baby, Vicki. Dot has been shopping. Vicki appeared sixteen years later as a teenager returning from the USA.

As you read, consider these key features:

Word level

- Look for the occasional use of figurative language in the text. Ethel says at one point on page 24, 'All my life people have treated me like I was ten paces behind.' What does she mean by this?

Sentence level

- Look at how different sentence structures are used at different times. Sometimes, a longer description uses a variety of verbs to paint a vivid picture, for example, when Dot says on page 26: 'She had a barrow, wore a black cap, could fight like a man and she did too … .'

Text level

- The text is very rich and features both the mundane (cups of tea, fig rolls) and the serious (murder, key information about other characters such as Lou and Pete).

- Sometimes the speech is very brief and basic: are these sections any less dramatic or powerful?

- Can you identify times when humour follows something dark or dramatic?

- Look for examples of Dot's references to religious matters: how do these contrast with what Ethel says?

- Look at the significance of Ethel's final words in this scene. Is she only referring to the song?

Speaking and listening

- How are we aware of the *status* of each character? Who is in control of the scene? Does it change?

Episode 248
by Charlie Humphreys

Main Characters

Dot Cotton

Dot, the most famous smoker on the Square, and one of the few surviving characters from the early years as this book goes to press, has not had a happy life, but often seems the most resilient and optimistic of characters. Her first husband, Charlie, was no good, and their son, Nick, was at various times a drug addict, thief and murderer. Many years after this episode took place, Dot married Jim Branning. Has she found true happiness at last?

Ethel Skinner

Ethel, like Dot, was a familiar presence on the Square, almost like a Chorus, commenting on the trials and tribulations of those around her. For many years, accompanied by her pet dog, Willy, she represented the old East End. Ethel died in 2000 but she lives on in many of the characters' memories.

The Baby

The baby in this episode is Vicki Fowler, daughter of teenage mum, Michelle Fowler and 'Dirty Den' Watts, landlord of the Queen Vic. She returned to Albert Square in 2003.

[THE DOOR OPENS AND THE DISGRUNTLED DOT ENTERS, WET.

TAKES OFF HAT AND COAT AND HANGS THEM UP]

DOT: You'll be relieved to hear I've got your fig rolls. [cont]

[TURNS AND LOOKS AT ETHEL.

SEE ETHEL IN CHAIR, ALBUM ON LAP, HEAD BACK AND HER MOUTH OPEN AS STILL AS DEATH.

DOT IMMEDIATELY ASSUMES THAT ETHEL IS DEAD AND IS ACCORDINGLY SHOCKED.

PAUSE.

SILENCE]

DOT: [cont] [QUIETLY] Ethel? [PAUSE] Ethel?

[SHE RUSHES OUT OF FLAT.

LONG PAUSE. AND DOT RETURNS, PEEPING HEAD AROUND DOOR.

DOT TOUCHES ETHEL. THEN QUICKLY WITHDRAWS FINGER WITH A CRY OF DESPAIR AND PLACES HAND ON HEART]

[AS DOT KNEELS]

DOT: Oh my father in heaven. [cont]

[PUTS HAND TO FACE AND TURNS AWAY.

MUMBLES]

DOT: [cont]
Our Father which art in heaven,
Hallowed be thy name,
Thy kingdom come,
Thy will be done on earth as it is in heaven.
Forgive us, oh dear God forgive us – especially me ...
and of course dear Ethel who was a simple soul ...

[AND HEAR ETHEL'S VOICE OVER]

ETHEL: Did you get the fig rolls? [cont]

[DOT RISES IN FRIGHT.

DOT'S EXPRESSION IS FILLED WITH THE HATE OF
RELIEF.

DOT CRUMBLES AND BREAKS AND CRIES.

ETHEL RISES]

ETHEL: [cont] What on earth's the matter?

DOT: I thought you were ... [CAN'T GO ON]

ETHEL: Thought I was what?

DOT: I thought you was dead.

ETHEL: [AMAZED AT THIS]

    [DOT, ANOTHER OUTBURST OF TEARS, COVERS FACE.

    PAUSE]

ETHEL: I'm not ready to go yet. I just drew me pension.

DOT: I was frightened.

ETHEL: [PERPLEXED] What of?

DOT: I thought you was gone.

ETHEL: What's the matter Dot? [cont]

    [ETHEL HITS HER, THEN STEPS BACK SURPRISED AND CONFUSED.

    ETHEL HAND TO MOUTH AND SEEMING TO REVERT BACK TO THE ETHEL WE KNOW AND LOVE]

ETHEL: [cont] I'm so sorry, I ... Dot.

DOT: You hit me.

ETHEL: I didn't ...

DOT: You hit me.

ETHEL: Only because you were like you were, Dot. I didn't mean to hurt you. My brother – he didn't mean to hurt me. Sometimes you have to be cruel. I'm sorry. It hurts, doesn't it? [cont]

          [PAUSE.

          SILENCE]

     ETHEL: [cont] Shall I make us a cup of tea? Shall I?

          [SILENCE]

Do you want to go? Do you Dot? Don't go. I'll make us
a nice cup of tea.

          [HURRIES TO KETTLE]

DOT: What's happening today? What's happening?

          [LOOKS TOWARDS THE WINDOW AND THE RAIN]

ETHEL: We are friends, ain't we, Dot?

DOT: [QUIETLY] Of course.

          [ETHEL MOVES SLOWLY TO CHAIR]

ETHEL: I understand about you and Doctor Legg and
your Charlie.

DOT: [AGHAST] You heard.

ETHEL: No I didn't.

DOT: But you said you understood. [ACCUSINGLY] You
listened.

ETHEL: Yes I did listen. About when you were in
Wales. I listened about the spring and that. Oh I
didn't mean what I said about your Mum deserting you.

DOT: I don't mean that.

    [PAUSE]

Anyway you didn't say she deserted me. Is that what you think she ...

ETHEL: [FRUSTRATED] Oh. [STAMPS FOOT] I don't know what I think or mean about anything. I wish today never was. It's a horrible day. I hate the rain. I don't know what to do or what to say.

DOT: You just sit there. It's just I was frightened.

ETHEL: Well I don't know, do I?

DOT: Just you relax, I'll make the tea.

    [PICKS UP THEIR CUPS, GOES TO SINK AND STARTS TO
    RINSE THEM. LOOKS AT KETTLE SURPRISED]

You haven't switched it on.

ETHEL: [ANNOYED AND IRRITABLE] Oh I don't care.

DOT: Never mind. Dot will do it.

ETHEL: Dot will do it. Dot'll do it. Don't you speak to me like I'm a fool. I'm a person. All my life people have treated me as though I was ten paces behind. Lou looked at me like she was better than I am, you do as well.

DOT: [COAXINGLY] Ethel ...

ETHEL: You and Lou ... I only wanted to enjoy life. I never wanted to be taken seriously, I'm not a serious person. [cont]

    [PAUSE.

    HITS ARM OF CHAIR]

ETHEL: [cont] I just want to have fun. It's not true what you said about me and my William – I did care, of course I did. I just couldn't cope. I tried, I just couldn't.

DOT: You made your William a very happy man, God rest his soul.

ETHEL: Yes I did. He didn't care about dinner being late or if I said silly things. I didn't think they were silly. He just laughed. The thing is, I can make people laugh more than I can make 'em take me serious. And of course if I try to be serious, they laugh even more. [CALMING. COMING DOWN] So I give it best and I don't pretend. I can't be a you or Lou or anyone. I'm me.

DOT: [SMILES] And thank God for you.

    [PAUSE.

    KETTLE BOILS AGAIN.

    THE TWO LADIES LOOK AT EACH OTHER.

    PAUSE]

ETHEL: Two sugars please ... 'Ere we used to have some wonderful characters in the East End, you know.

DOT: Still have.

ETHEL: Oh no, not now! Sometimes I think it's only me and Lou left. [SMILES] Oh we used to have fun.

DOT: What I hear of it. It was all poverty, starvation, filth and squalor.

ETHEL: Never took no notice of that.

DOT: Do you want one of your [PAUSE] fig rolls?

ETHEL: No thanks, it's a bit late in the day. [cont]

[DOT CLOSES EYES, DISGUSTED]

ETHEL: [cont] I often think of 'em, you know, Banjo, Willie Straus, Old Mother Parkins. She had a barrow, wore a black cap, could fight like a man and she did too, sold ladies' undies. Her son Ron was **topped** at **Pentonville** for murdering a prostitute, oh lovely people. There was Arnie the bookie.

[DOT RETURNS WITH ETHEL'S TEA]

Mother Parkins beat him up for **welching** on a bet. Then, of course, later on there was Pat, Lou never wanted Pete to marry Pat.

DOT: I remember Pat when she was courting Pete.

ETHEL: Do you remember Den's Dad, Dennis?

DOT: Course.

ETHEL: He was a hard man. Wasn't he?

DOT: Well, he gave Den a few thick ears.

ETHEL: Aye. [LOOKS AWAY REMEMBERING]

  [DOT SMILES]

ETHEL: Remember Lou when Arthur wanted to marry Pauline?

  [DOT **X'S** TO SIT]

DOT: Lou's always been the same. Do you remember Pete when he wanted to marry Kathy?

ETHEL: She's mellowed has Lou.

DOT: Thank God.

  [PAUSE.

  SILENCE]

ETHEL: Banjo, Mother Parkins, Willie Straus, all gone, lots more.

DOT: [SMILES] It's the way of the flesh Ethel. Thank God we got a soul. I just hope they weigh up the good against the bad. I must've done many more good things in life than bad.

ETHEL: [KNOWINGLY] It doesn't matter. You know.

DOT: [**TAKING UMBRAGE**] It doesn't matter! 'Course it matters. Haven't you got any faith?

ETHEL: [PAUSE] I'd like to see my William again. Mother Parkins was very good to me and always I thought Old Den was handsome. [cont]

[PAUSE AND LONG SILENCE]

ETHEL: [cont] And I'd like to tell Mum and Dad I didn't really mind about my things.

DOT: [SAGELY] They know Ethel, they know.

ETHEL: Do they?

[PAUSE]

It's good then.

[PAUSE. LONG SILENCE]

I miss the East End you know.

DOT: You miss youth Ethel, youth.

ETHEL: [THINKS ABOUT THIS. THEN] Do I? I feel the same.

DOT: [ALARMED] What's the time?

ETHEL: Oh my God we missed her medicine.

DOT: Where is it?

ETHEL: It's here.

[RISES AND MOVES TO CABINET, PICKS UP BOTTLE AND RETURNS TO BABY]

DOT: I'll hold her. You pour it.

ETHEL: Yes. Here we are.

DOT: You give it to her.

ETHEL: She doesn't want it Dot.

DOT: Well what shall we do?

    [ETHEL LOOKS AT BABY AND STARTS TO SING]

ETHEL: 'She's only a bird in a golden cage, a beautiful sight to see.'

    [AND DOT JOINS IN]

ETHEL & DOT: 'She thinks she's happy and free from care
She's not what she seems to be ... .'

    [THEY BOTH HUM QUIETLY AND BABY IS PLACED IN CARRYCOT.

    THEY BOTH BEND DOWN TO CHILD]

DOT: Ethel?

ETHEL: Yes.

DOT: You may borrow my brolly.

ETHEL: Oh ta.

[DOT SMILES AND THE BABY CRIES]

ETHEL: [STARTS TO SING]
'She's only a bird in a ...'

DOT: [STARTS TO SING]
'It's sad when you think of her wasted life ...'

[BOTH LADIES FROWN AT EACH OTHER THAT THEY HAVE
STARTED DIFFERENTLY]

From the beginning then.

[ETHEL SHAKES HEAD SADLY.

PAUSE]

ETHEL: ... Never again Dot. Never from the beginning.

Titles:

Cindy leaves the Square

Writer: Tony McHale

Transmission date: 17 October 1996

loss and departure

About the text

Type: Group and individual

Episodes in which central characters leave – either forever, or for a number of years – are usually charged with emotion and lots of action. In this episode, written by Tony McHale, a number of storylines come to a head. Cindy, Ian's wife, has hired a contract killer to shoot him. She has been having an affair with David Wicks. However, the attempt fails, and Cindy, fearing she will be imprisoned, wants to escape, taking two of her children with her. She is forced to leave Lucy, her other child, behind.

Word level

- Look at the use of idiomatic words and phrases such as, 'yapping' and 'over the top'. This is true even of some of the stage directions (for example, 'GRANT PULLING OUT ALL THE STOPS').

- Consider the way in which the same phrases, when repeated, can be interpreted in different ways, for example, when Cindy says, 'Yeah – you're right. You are just the same.'

Sentence level

- Find uses of ellipses (…) both for pauses in speech and for interruptions. These are particularly prevalent in contemporary dramatic writing.

Text level

- Note the way in which Mason's speech is representative of his role as a police officer, for example, his more formal way of speaking, 'I understand your anxiety …' on page 38.

- Look at how different elements of the action are advanced during this series of scenes. Note, for example, what we learn about Phil's motives in helping Ian, and what he really thinks (see page 40).

- Note how we learn about different characters not only through what they say about themselves, but also through how this is then reflected back by someone else's response. For example, see David's speech to Cindy when he says, 'I let people down …' on page 43.

- Look at the information provided by the writer to the actors and director in the stage directions, particularly at the end of the scene. Note the contrast between Cindy and her children.

Episode 401 by Tony McHale

Ian and Cindy in an earlier episode.

Main Characters

David Wicks – Pat Evans' son, Cindy's lover

Ian Beale – local entrepreneur
Cindy Beale – his wife
Steven Beale
Peter Beale } her children
Lucy Beale

Phil Mitchell – owner of The Arches garage, husband of Kathy, Ian's mother
Grant Mitchell – his brother
Kathy Mitchell – Ian Beale's mother, Phil's wife

Mason – police officer

Roy Evans – local car dealer
Pat Evans – David Wicks' mother, Kathy's friend, Roy's wife
Barry Evans – Roy's son

SCENE: 401/38. INT. BARRY'S CAR. DAY [11.03am]

LOCATION:

    [CINDY IS STILL IN THE BACK OF THE CAR WITH STEVEN AND PETER.

    BARRY DRIVES, DAVID NEXT TO HIM.

    THERE IS SILENCE]

DAVID: I managed to get some money.

CINDY: How much?

DAVID: Two and half grand.

CINDY: Is that all?

DAVID: It's all I could get.

CINDY: That won't last us long.

DAVID: Cindy – this is the second lot of cash I've coughed up for you in as many months.

CINDY: So?

DAVID: So I don't think I'm doing too bad.

CINDY: You don't really understand what's happening here, do you?

DAVID: Yes I do.

CINDY: I'm giving up everything ... and you're giving up nothing.

DAVID: Whose fault's that? You were the one getting carried away. Getting him shot was crazy. Anything we had, you and me, anything ... was destroyed the minute you handed over the cash to whoever. That was over the top ... well over the top.

CINDY: I tried to stop it, I knew it was stupid. I did try and stop it David ... but it was too late.

DAVID: You should never have started it. For weeks you went on about how it was all going to be fine. How you would have the children, how he would give you money, how you were entitled to this and that – then suddenly nothing. What changed?

CINDY: Everything.

DAVID: Well I didn't change. I was just the same. I knew the score. I knew what was what. We could have been alright, it was you that lost it. Not me. I'm just the same.

CINDY: [A BEAT] Yeah – you're right. You are just the same.

[THE CAR CONTINUES ON ITS WAY]

SCENE 401/39. EXT. THE SQUARE/CAR LOT. DAY. [11.05am]

LOT

[PHIL IS TRYING THE PORTAKABIN DOOR. IT'S LOCKED.

GRANT IS STANDING BY HIS CAR]

GRANT: He's gone with her.

PHIL: But where?

GRANT: Anywhere ... who knows. We could just wait here for Barry to come back and collect his car, and then beat it out of him.

[PHIL CROSSES TO BARRY'S CAR]

PHIL: If Barry's any sense he'll have gone with them.

GRANT: That'll be cosy ... the three of them.

[PHIL OPENS THE DOOR TO BARRY'S CAR]

PHIL: Not very security conscious, our Barry.

[PHIL STARTS TO SEARCH THE CAR]

GRANT: He's not got anything worth stealing, that's why.

[PHIL FINDS A LEAFLET IN THE GLOVE COMPARTMENT]

PHIL: Got it.

GRANT: What?

PHIL: Eurostar timetable. Let's go.

[PHIL AND GRANT GO AND JUMP IN GRANT'S CAR]

<u>SCENE: 401/40. INT. PAT AND ROY'S HOUSE. DAY.</u>
<u>[11.25am]</u>

<u>STUDIO D</u>

    [THE POLICE HAVE ARRIVED. THE CHILDREN ARE NOW
UPSTAIRS.

    MASON IS TALKING TO IAN.

    PAT AND KATHY ARE THERE]

<u>IAN</u>: I don't know, about ten thirty I suppose.

<u>MASON</u>: So they've been gone an hour.

<u>IAN</u>: About that.

<u>MASON</u>: Have you spoken to her since she picked up the children?

<u>IAN</u>: I spoke to her on the phone.

<u>MASON</u>: And what did she say?

<u>IAN</u>: Nothing.

<u>MASON</u>: She didn't say she was taking the children away?

<u>IAN</u>: No.

<u>MASON</u>: So we don't really know that's what she's done.

<u>KATHY</u>: That's what she's done alright. She's been planning it for days.

<u>MASON</u>: But at this moment, we don't know for certain that's what she's done.

IAN: I know, I know for certain.

[ROY RETURNS HOME]

ROY: What's going on?

PAT: Cindy's run off with Steven and Peter.

ROY: Oh God.

MASON: Where's her family?

KATHY: Devon.

MASON: Do you think she'll have gone there?

KATHY: She could have done.

IAN: No.

MASON: We can get that checked out.

IAN: I've told you she won't go there. That would be too obvious. She knows that's the first place I'd look.

MASON: So where? Friends? Who are her friends?

KATHY: Well there's Gita ... she lives ...

IAN: [CUTTING ACROSS] Just get out there and look for her.

MASON: I understand your anxiety, but I'm trying to **ascertain** ...

IAN: Listen to me. If we don't find her soon, I will never see my children again, do you understand that? She is not going to her parents ... or her friends ... or anywhere you're going to find her by knocking on a few doors. She's not an idiot ... she's planned this, and the longer you stand here yapping about it, the further she gets from Walford.

MASON: I think if we can just try and keep calm.

IAN: Calm ... calm! I've been shot at, my wife has run off with two of my kids ... I have lost everything ... and you tell me to be calm ... I have nothing ... I have nothing!

[IAN DOUBLES UP IN PAIN, COLLAPSING IN A CHAIR]

KATHY: Somebody get an ambulance.

[IAN CAN'T SPEAK HE'S IN SO MUCH PAIN]

MASON: I'll call it in.

[KATHY MOVES IAN, TRYING TO COMFORT HIM]

KATHY: I'm sorry, I'm sorry Ian ... I'm sorry.

[IAN GRITS HIS TEETH AS THE PAIN INCREASES]

SCENE: 401/41. EXT. WATERLOO STATION. DAY. [11.30am]

LOCATION

[BARRY'S **GRANADA** PULLS UP OUTSIDE WATERLOO STATION.

CINDY, DAVID, PETER AND STEVEN CLAMBER OUT.

BARRY STAYS PUT]

BARRY: Good luck Cindy.

CINDY: Thanks.

BARRY: It's been ... different.

DAVID: Get off. I'll be alright.

    [CINDY, DAVID, PETER AND STEVEN HEAD OFF INTO THE STATION, AS BARRY PULLS AWAY]

SCENE: 401/42. INT. GRANT'S CAR. DAY.   [11.32am]

LOCATION

    [THE CAR IS SPEEDING ITS WAY TOWARDS WATERLOO.

    GRANT PULLING OUT ALL THE STOPS]

GRANT: How was it with Kathy?

PHIL: She's moving back in.

GRANT: I told you. I knew yesterday she was warming to it ... when she thanked you for nailing that John geezer. Mind you, I was impressed. I didn't think you even liked Ian.

PHIL: I don't. I don't give a monkey's about him. I feel more sorry for Cindy having had to put up with him all these years. But I know Kathy ... I know what she thinks about him ... and I know what she thinks about Cindy ... and I wanted her and Ben back ... Pretending to be bothered about the mess Ian's got himself into is a small price to pay really.

GRANT: My advice is never tell her.

PHIL: Do you take me for stupid?

[PHIL SMILES AS GRANT CONCENTRATES ON THE ROAD]

SCENE: 401/43. EXT. WATERLOO STATION CONCOURSE. DAY. [11.33am]

LOCATION

[CINDY ON HER WAY TO THE EUROTUNNEL CHECK-IN.

DAVID, PETER IN HIS ARMS, HANDS HER £2500 OF THE MONEY HE MADE FROM FISHER EARLIER]

SCENE: 401/44. EXT. THE SQUARE. DAY. [11.34am]

LOT

[AN AMBULANCE IS PARKED OUTSIDE PAT'S HOUSE. KATHY, PAT AND ROY WATCH AS IAN IS LOADED ABOARD THE AMBULANCE.

KATHY IS HELPED IN BEHIND HIM, THE DOORS ARE CLOSED, THE LIGHTS FLASH AND AWAY IT GOES]

<u>SCENE: 401/45. EXT. WATERLOO STATION. EUROSTAR
CHECK-IN. DAY.</u> [11.35am]

<u>LOCATION</u>

 [CINDY HOLDING STEVEN'S HAND, DAVID STILL
 CARRYING PETER.

 CINDY LOOKS AT DAVID. HE IS TRYING TO AVOID HER
 EYES.

 CINDY IS VERY AWARE OF HER CHILDREN'S PRESENCE.

 DAVID LEANS FORWARD AND KISSES CINDY ON THE LIPS
 - LIGHTLY]

<u>DAVID:</u> Take care Cindy.

<u>CINDY:</u> So this is it?

<u>DAVID:</u> Afraid so.

<u>CINDY:</u> This is what the last two years have been all
about.

<u>DAVID:</u> I wish it could have been different.

<u>CINDY:</u> Do you?

<u>DAVID:</u> Yeah.

<u>CINDY:</u> Then come with me.

 [DAVID LOOKS AT CINDY]

<u>DAVID:</u> You know I can't.

<u>CINDY:</u> Why not?

<u>DAVID:</u> It wouldn't work out, not now.

<u>CINDY:</u> We can get over what's happened.

DAVID: No. We'll never get over some of the things we've said, some of the things we've done.

CINDY: Please, for me, come with me. I'll make you happy, I promise.

[DAVID GENTLY SHAKES HIS HEAD]

DAVID: I wish I could, but I can't.

CINDY: Why not?

DAVID: Don't you understand Cindy ... this is what I do. I let people down. I've made a habit of it all my life. If I went with you now, then it would happen all over again. I would let you down. I don't want to do that to you.

CINDY: [NODS] Great excuse David, great excuse.

[SHE TAKES PETER FROM HIS ARMS AND GOES THROUGH INTO THE CHECKOUT.

DAVID STANDS THERE.

JUST BEFORE CINDY DISAPPEARS FROM VIEW, SHE TURNS BACK TO LOOK AT HIM.

FOR A MOMENT IT LOOKS LIKE DAVID MIGHT GO, THEN CINDY IS GONE, AND ALONG WITH IT THE MOMENT]

SCENE: 401/46. EXT. WATERLOO STATION. DAY. [11.55am]

LOCATION

[GRANT'S CAR PULLS UP OUTSIDE THE STATION.

PHIL AND GRANT JUMP OUT OF THE CAR AND HEAD INTO THE STATION]

SCENE: 401/47. EXT. EUROSTAR CHECK-IN. DAY. [11.57am]

LOCATION

[DAVID WHO HAS JUST BEEN STOOD THERE, MOVES AWAY FROM THE CHECK-IN AS THE TRAIN PULLS AWAY FROM THE PLATFORM.

HE DOESN'T KNOW WHAT TO THINK AS HE STARTS TO CROSS BACK THROUGH THE STATION. PART OF HIM IS VERY RELIEVED AND THERE'S ANOTHER PART OF HIM CONFUSED, ANGRY AND UPSET.

HE DOESN'T SEE PHIL AND GRANT COME RUNNING ONTO THE CONCOURSE AND HEAD FOR THE CHECK-IN.

GRANT AND PHIL REALISE THEY'RE TOO LATE!

DAVID, UNAWARE OF THEM, CONTINUES ON HIS WAY]

GRANT: What do we do now?

PHIL: Let her go. We tried. Kathy'll know we tried. Good luck to her, that's what I say.

[PHIL AND GRANT TURN AND LEAVE AS THE TRAIN DISAPPEARS]

SCENE: 401/48. INT. TRAIN. DAY. [11.58am]

LOCATION

[STEVEN AND PETER ARE HAPPILY COLOURING IN SOME PICTURES. THIS IS STILL AN ADVENTURE.

CINDY STARES OUT OF THE WINDOW, TRYING TO HOLD ON.

SHE REACHES INTO HER BAG FOR A TISSUE, AND PULLS OUT LUCY'S DOLLY.

CINDY CAN'T CONTAIN HER PAIN.

THE TEARS FLOW FREELY]

44

Ricky and Bianca's Wedding Morning

Writer: Tony Jordan

Transmission date: 17 April 1997

marriage and comedy

About the text

Type: Group

Marriages are part of the staple diet of soaps, as in life. Waiting to see what will go wrong, who will make a fool of himself or herself, what skeletons will come out of the closet … all make for good drama. However, often the build-up to the wedding is as important as the event itself. This extract from the beginning of an episode by Tony Jordan deals with the morning of the wedding between Ricky and Bianca, and, in particular, the repercussions of Ricky's stag night. Here, the drama is balanced with humour.

Word level

- Unusually, French – or a form of French – is used at various points during this episode. Are we able to tell what is going on?

- Note, too, the images created by the writer in the stage directions to suggest how he sees the scenes in his mind (for example, the 'spray of light' sent into Bianca's room).

Sentence level

- Look at the way punctuation is used to emphasise Ricky's anger and despair, especially the use of exclamation marks, as well as short punchy sentences, for example, 'I'm dead.'

Text level

- Note the constrasting sequence of scenes, moving from Bianca waking safely in her bed on her wedding day to Ricky waking to find himself in a field.

- Can you identify any moments of dramatic irony – when we know the truth about the situation and the other characters do not? Does this create tension, humour – or both?

- Humour is created in many ways: through situation, through characterisation (Nigel's attempts at French, for example) and through the way the action unfolds – including the punchline revealing where Ricky and the others really are.

Episode 479
by Tony Jordan

Main Characters

Bianca Jackson – the bride
Carol Jackson – her mother

Ricky Butcher – the groom
Nigel Bates – close friend of Grant Mitchell and Ricky

Phil Mitchell – owner of The Arches garage and Ricky's best man
Grant Mitchell – landlord of the Queen Vic

Tiffany – Bianca's bridesmaid

Jon – young Frenchman
Gerald – farmer

Happy together: Ricky and Bianca at a speedway race.

SCENE: 479/1. INT. JACKSONS'. DAY. [8.27am]

STUDIO D

[OPEN ON **CU** OF BIANCA – IN BED FAST ASLEEP, A HINT
OF A SMILE – THE KIND OF SMILE RESERVED FOR
A BRIDE ON HER WEDDING DAY ...

A MOMENT, THEN WIDEN SHOT TO REVEAL CAROL AS SHE
SITS ON EDGE OF BED, PUTTING THE CUP OF TEA ON THE
BEDSIDE TABLE.

SHE GENTLY ROCKS BIANCA, WHOSE EYES OPEN SLOWLY]

BIANCA: [SLEEPILY] Mmmm?

[SHE FOCUSES ON CAROL]

What time is it?

CAROL: Half eight ...

BIANCA: Mmmm ...

CAROL: [GENTLY] You're getting married today
remember ... ?

BIANCA: Mmmm ...

[CAROL SMILES – LEANS OVER AND PECKS BIANCA ON
CHEEK.

BEFORE SHE LEAVES, SHE OPENS CURTAINS, SENDING
SPRAY OF LIGHT INTO THE ROOM AND SHE'S GONE.

OUT ON A SLEEPY BUT HAPPY AND CONTENTED BIANCA ...]

CU close up

48

SCENE: 479/2. EXT. FIELD. DAY. [8.30am]

LOCATION

     [EXTREME CU OF RICKY - FAST ASLEEP.

     IT'S A TROUBLED SLEEP, THE KIND OF TROUBLED SLEEP
     RESERVED FOR A GROOM ON HIS WEDDING DAY ...

     STIRRING, EYEBALLS FLICKERING BEHIND CLOSED LIDS,
     THEN SLOWLY OPENING.

     DISORIENTATED, HE LOOKS AROUND.

     CU OF GRANT, SNORING - PAN DOWN TO NIGEL'S HEAD
     ON GRANT'S CHEST, ASLEEP AND SMILING AT
     CINDY CRAWFORD'S REQUEST FOR MORE SEX ... . DOWN
     TO PHIL, HIS HEAD DRAPED OVER NIGEL ...

     THEN BACK TO RICKY, BLINKING, TRYING TO TAKE IN
     INFORMATION.

     SUDDENLY IT HITS HIM.

     WIDEN SHOT AS HE SITS BOLT UPRIGHT TO REVEAL THEY
     ARE ALL LYING IN THE MIDDLE OF A FIELD ... .

     SUDDEN PANIC FROM RICKY - HE SPINS ROUND ... .
     NOT A BUILDING IN SIGHT.

     HE'S CLEARLY VERY COLD.

     HE STARTS SHAKING THE OTHERS, WHO SLOWLY COME
     ROUND]

RICKY: Phil ... . Wake up ...

[VARIOUS GRUNTS AND MOANS ETC., AS THEY REGAIN CONSCIOUSNESS, AND BEGIN TO SIT UP]

GRANT: It's freezing.

PHIL: What time is it?

RICKY: Half eight ... Have you seen where we are?

[PHIL, GRANT AND NIGEL LOOK AROUND THEM WITH LETTERBOX EYES]

GRANT: We're in a field.

RICKY: I know we're in a field, but how did we get here?

[PHIL, GRANT AND NIGEL LOOK AT EACH OTHER, BUT IT'S CLEAR THEY HAVE NO IDEA]

RICKY: [SUDDENLY REMEMBERS – LOOKS AT WATCH AGAIN] I'm getting married in three and a half hours ...

PHIL: Whoops ...

RICKY: I'm dead.

NIGEL: What are we doing in a field?

RICKY: How the hell do I know? You lot were supposed to be looking after me ...

[ON PHIL, LOOKING AND FEELING AWFUL, NOW ADDING GUILT TO THE LIST]

PHIL: Alright ... Look ... We know we're in a field right? The question is ... Where's the field?

　　　[THEY ALL STAND, AND LOOK AROUND THEM – NO SIGN OF CIVILISATION

　　　PANIC SETTING IN]

RICKY: What we gonna do?

PHIL: Er ... Find a phone box ...

GRANT: And a cafe ... . I've got a throat like a miner's jockstrap ...

PHIL: There must be a house or something somewhere ...

RICKY: There isn't ... Look!

　　　[WALKS AWAY FROM GROUP AND BACK AGAIN
　　　EXASPERATED ...]

We could be anywhere ...

PHIL: [STILL SUFFERING] Alright! Let's just think about this for a minute ... We're in a field, so there must be a farm or something somewhere ... So there must be a farmhouse, or a road ...

GRANT: Yeah, but which way ... ?

PHIL: I dunno, you were in the army ... Can't you work it out?

GRANT: Eh?

PHIL: When you were doing exercises and that ... . Say you were stranded, didn't know where you were ... What would you do?

GRANT: Ask for a helicopter.

PHIL: Oh, that's a great help ...

GRANT: Well we had maps and compasses and things ...

RICKY: Phil!

PHIL: Yeah, right ...

　　[LOOKS AROUND]

Er ... . That way ... .

　　[RICKY STRIDES AWAY – THE OTHERS START TRUDGING
　　AFTER HIM.

　　OUT AS THEY WALK ACROSS FIELD ...]

SCENE: 479/3. INT. JACKSONS'. DAY. [8.45am]

STUDIO D

　　[CAROL IS AT COOKER FRYING EGGS, THE TABLE IS SET
　　FOR BREAKFAST –

　　LAID OUT SPECIALLY FOR ONE, NAPKINS, ORANGE JUICE
　　ETC.

　　BIANCA ENTERS IN DRESSING GOWN, LOOKING LESS THAN
　　GLAMOROUS ...]

BIANCA: Morning ...

CAROL: How d'you feel?

BIANCA: Better than I thought I would ... Just a bit of a headache ...

CAROL: I'll get you some paracetamol ...

BIANCA: [SHE SEES THE TABLE] What's all this?

CAROL: It's for you ... Sit yourself down ...

BIANCA: [SITTING] What about everyone else?

CAROL: We've all had ours ...

BIANCA: You didn't have to do all this ...

CAROL: 'Course I did ... It's your wedding day.

 [CAROL PUTS TWO PILLS AND GLASS OF WATER IN FRONT OF HER – BIANCA TAKES THEM]

BIANCA: D'you think I should phone Ricky? See if he's up?

CAROL: Don't you dare ... . You're not supposed to see or talk to him 'til you get to the church ... Besides, him and Phil were staying at Nigel's ... They'll make sure he's up ...

BIANCA: If he's late I'll kill him ...

CAROL: He won't be ...

 [A BEAT.

 CAROL PUTS HUGE COOKED BREAKFAST IN FRONT OF HER – BIANCA LOOKS AT IT – SLIGHTLY QUEASY ...]

CAROL: You can't get married on an empty stomach ...

 [OUT ON BIANCA]

SCENE: 479/4. EXT. FIELD. DAY. [8.45am]

LOCATION

    [PHIL, GRANT, RICKY AND NIGEL TRUDGING ACROSS
    FIELD ... STILL NO SIGN OF CIVILISATION]

RICKY: I don't believe it, there must be something somewhere ... .

    [PHIL GLANCES AT RICKY – CLEARLY FEELING GUILTY]

NIGEL: Maybe there was a nuclear war while we were asleep, and we're the only ones left ...

GRANT: It wouldn't be so bad if we knew where we were ... .

PHIL: Look, we're bound to hit a road soon, we've been walking for quarter of an hour ...

RICKY: I'm dead ... .

NIGEL: Here ... Maybe we're still asleep ... This is just a dream, when in reality we're tucked up in bed ...

GRANT: You must have some sick dreams ... .

NIGEL: Well, now you come to mention it ... . I had this one once, where ...

PHIL: Not now Nige ...

    [A BEAT]

What I don't understand is how we got here in the first place ...

GRANT: Last thing I remember was in the strip club ...

PHIL: And those two geezers ... What were their names? Ken ...

GRANT: Ken and Wayne ...

[PHIL AND GRANT STOP DEAD IN TRACKS]

PHIL: You thinking what I'm thinking?

RICKY: What?

GRANT: They were on their way to Dover ...

RICKY: Please don't tell me we're in Dover ...

[A LOOK BETWEEN PHIL AND GRANT]

GRANT: Does anyone remember getting on a boat?

RICKY: What?

[A BEAT, THEN HE REALISES]

RICKY: No! Phil ... . Tell him to stop winding me up ...

NIGEL: This ain't funny ...

GRANT: You see anyone laughing?

[A BEAT – THE AWFULNESS SETS IN – RICKY SUDDENLY LAUNCHES AT PHIL, PUSHING HIM BACKWARDS]

RICKY: This is your fault!

[RICKY LASHES OUT AT PHIL - GRANT AND NIGEL RUSH FORWARD TO TRY AND PULL HIM OFF]

RICKY: I'm supposed to be getting married ... . You can't do this to me ...

GRANT: Alright Ricky, that's enough ...

RICKY: I didn't even want to come out ... You made me!

[PHIL DOESN'T RETALIATE - HE KNOWS HE'S LET RICKY DOWN]

GRANT: [HOLDING RICKY WITH DIFFICULTY] This ain't gonna solve anything is it?

RICKY: You've ruined everything!

[TAKE PHIL'S REACTION]

NIGEL: Wait! What's that?

RICKY: What?

NIGEL: Ssshh ... Listen.

[THEY ALL STAND STILL, STRAINING TO LISTEN - RICKY SHRUGS GRANT OFF.

A DOG CAN BE HEARD BARKING]

PHIL: Where's it coming from ... ?

GRANT: Over there ...

[THEY ALL BREAK OUT INTO A RUN - RUNNING IN THE DIRECTION OF THE SOUND.

THEY CROSS THE BROW OF A HILL/PASS THROUGH A HEDGEROW ... . AND SEE A YOUNG MAN, JON, THROWING STICKS FOR A DOG]

RICKY: Over there ... .

[THEY RUN OVER TOWARDS JON SHOUTING - HE STOPS AND WAITS FOR THEM TO JOIN HIM]

PHIL: Are we glad to see you ... .

[JON SMILES]

PHIL: Can you tell us where we are?

JON: Je suis desolé, je ne parle pas Anglais ...

[TAKE REACTIONS - STUNNED]

PHIL: Do what?

JON: Je suis Francais ... .

NIGEL: It's a frog ... .

RICKY: Oh no!

[PHIL AND GRANT EXCHANGE A LOOK - WHOOPS!]

RICKY: I knew it! We're in France ...

[WALKS AWAY]

No ... . Please tell me this isn't happening ...

PHIL: Hang on ... Let me think ...

    [A BEAT, THEN TO JON, SLOWLY]

Where are we?

    [JON SHRUGS]

PHIL: [POINTS TO FLOOR] France? Er, Francais ... .

GRANT: Ask him where the ferry is ...

PHIL: [TO JON] Where's the ferry?

JON: Ferry? Je ne comprends pas ... Er ... Je suis étudiant ...

PHIL: I don't think he knows ...

Sticking together: Grant and Phil Mitchell.

GRANT: Alright ... Ask him if there's a phone anywhere ...

PHIL: [TO JON] Is there ... .

[HE STOPS MID SENTENCE, REALISING ... . TURNS TO GRANT]

Why don't you ask him ... ?

GRANT: [TO JON] Er ... Telephono? Une telephono?

JON: [BEMUSED, THEN] Ah! Téléphone?

GRANT: Si Si Telefon ... .

[PHIL AND NIGEL EXCHANGE A LOOK – WONDERING WHY GRANT IS USING SPANISH]

JON: Ah ... Il y a une ferme ... une maison près du ...

[PHIL AND GRANT NONE THE WISER]

NIGEL: He said there's a house over there ...

[EVERYONE TURNS TO LOOK AT NIGEL DUMBFOUNDED]

[BY WAY OF EXPLANATION] He said maison ... . That's a house.

GRANT: You can talk French?

NIGEL: I helped Clare with her homework once ...

PHIL: Why didn't you say anything?

NIGEL: You seemed to be doing alright ...

GRANT: Ask him how far ... ?

NIGEL: Right ...

    [NIGEL PUSHES TO FRONT, CEREMONIOUSLY TAKING CHARGE]

NIGEL: Bonjour ...

JON: Bonjour ...

    [NIGEL TURNS TO LOOK AT PHIL AND GRANT – WINKS.

    HE THEN TURNS BACK TO JON]

NIGEL: [FRENCH ACCENT] Er ... How far?

JON: Je suis desolé, je ne parle pas Anglais ... Je ne comprends pas ... .

GRANT: What did he say ... ?

NIGEL: I'm not sure ... It's a funny dialect ...

PHIL: It's called French ...

JON: Voilà ...

    [HE POINTS TOWARDS DIRECTION OF FARMHOUSE]

NIGEL: Over there ... .

PHIL: Come on then ... .

NIGEL: [TO JON] Mercy ...

    [JON SMILES]

JON: Au revoir ...

    [THEY START WALKING IN DIRECTION INDICATED BY JON.

    RICKY, COMPLETELY DEFLATED]

RICKY: What am I gonna do?

PHIL: Look, we'll get you there alright?

RICKY: How?

PHIL: I dunno ... Look, with a bit of luck we're not too far inland, and we're still near Calais ... If we can get on a hovercraft, or Eurostar or something, we can still make it.

GRANT: How long we got?

PHIL: [CHECKS WATCH] Three hours ...

    [OUT AS THEY SCURRY ACROSS FIELD]

SCENE: 479/5. INT. JACKSONS'. DAY. [9.00am]

STUDIO D

    [BIANCA HAS NOW FINISHED BREAKFAST, SHE AND CAROL
    SITTING AT TABLE]

BIANCA: I wonder what he's doing now ... ?

CAROL: Judging by the state of Robbie when he got home, taking something for his hangover I shouldn't wonder ...

BIANCA: I didn't hear Robbie come in ...

CAROL: Alan dropped him off ... He said Phil and Ricky left early and went home ...

BIANCA: Alan ... ?

CAROL: Mmm hmm ...

BIANCA: So what time's he coming?

CAROL: He's already here.

BIANCA: What?

   [ON CAROL - A LITTLE SELF-CONSCIOUS]

He stayed?

CAROL: Well it was late ...

   [A MOMENT BETWEEN THEM - THEY EMBRACE]

BIANCA: Oh Mum ...

CAROL: Don't build your hopes up ... He slept on the sofa ... But it's a start.

   [THE DOOR OPENS - TIFFANY ENTERS]

TIFFANY: Oh ... Shall I go out and come back in again ... ?

   [CAROL AND BIANCA PART]

CAROL: No, you're alright ... come in ...

TIFFANY: Only if you're having one of those touching mother and daughter moments, I don't mind waiting ...

CAROL: [GLANCE AT BIANCA] I think we've finished now.

TIFFANY: Good. So how's the blushing bride then?

CAROL: A bit hungover, but she's had her breakfast ...

TIFFANY: Right, well I've come to make her beautiful ...

[LOOKS CLOSELY AT BIANCA]

I've come early ...

BIANCA: Flamin' cheek ...

CAROL: You'd better go up and have a bath first ...

BIANCA: [STANDS] Okay ...

TIFFANY: Any news from the boy wonder yet then?

BIANCA: [WALKING TO DOOR] Mum was just saying ... He left early last night and went home ... .

TIFFANY: Got him well trained haven't you?

BIANCA: Well you've got to ain't you ... ? He'd only get himself in trouble otherwise ...

[AND BIANCA'S GONE.

OUT ON CAROL – SMILING]

SCENE: 479/6. EXT. FARMYARD. DAY. [9.02am]

LOCATION

    [RICKY, PHIL, GRANT AND NIGEL ARE WALKING THROUGH FARMYARD TOWARDS FARMHOUSE]

RICKY: A quiet drink you said ... And we end up in France ...

PHIL: That's right, blame me ...

RICKY: You're supposed to be my best man ... And what was all that stuff on the bus? "Don't worry, I'll look after you ... I'm not drinking ... ."

PHIL: Alright, so I had a few ...

RICKY: A "few"?

    [PHIL LOOKING VERY SHEEPISH]

GRANT: Look, arguing amongst ourselves ain't gonna help is it? We're here ... What we have to do now is work out how to get back ...

PHIL: All we need is a car, and directions to the hovercraft, or train station ... Nige ... You do all the talking ...

NIGEL: Why me?

PHIL: You know more French than we do ...

GRANT: That ain't difficult.

RICKY: Maybe we should phone home ... Tell 'em to postpone it or something ...

PHIL: Let's find out where we are first.

RICKY: I can't have Bianca turning up at the church on her own ...

PHIL: Alright ... . We'll phone if we have to ...

[THEY REACH FRONT DOOR OF FARMHOUSE, THEY STEP ASIDE TO LET NIGEL THROUGH.

A BEAT, THEN HE KNOCKS, DOGS START BARKING.

A MOMENT, BEFORE THE DOOR OPENS AND A FARMER GERALD OPENS THE DOOR]

NIGEL: Ah ... Bonjour messieur ...

[GERALD LOOKS AT HIM BLANKLY, NIGEL CONTINUES IN A SLOW FRENCH ACCENT]

NIGEL: Er ... We are ... Anglais, and avey vous un lost ... . Je suis un hovercraft ... hovercraft ... ?

[MAKES WHOOSHING SOUND]

Avec moi, and une comrades, requiray vous une train ... ? Si vous plais? Train?

[MAKES TRAIN NOISE.

A BEAT, THEN GERALD LOOKS BACK OVER HIS SHOULDER]

GERALD: Philippe ... It's some of your lot ... .

[GRANT, PHIL, NIGEL AND RICKY LOOK AT EACH OTHER DUMBFOUNDED]

GRANT: You speak English?

[PHILIPPE, A YOUNG FRENCHMAN, APPEARS BESIDE GERALD]

PHIL: Hang on ... I'm confused here ... Where are we?

GERALD: Town Farm.

GRANT: Yeah but where? Which country?

RICKY: We're lost ...

GERALD: You must be if you don't even know which country you're in ...

[GERALD LOOKS AT FOUR EXPECTANT FACES]

GERALD: You're in South Ewellford.

GRANT: England?

GERALD: Kent.

[AS THE INFORMATION SINKS IN ... RICKY IS OVERJOYED]

RICKY: Yes!

[HE TURNS AND HUGS PHIL, JUMPING UP AND DOWN - PHIL AND GRANT DO THE SAME, OBLIVIOUS TO GERALD'S BEMUSED EXPRESSION. THEN]

PHIL: Er, have you got a phone ... ?

GERALD: You'd better come in ...

[OUT AS THEY ENTER - CONSIDERABLY HAPPIER]

5

Tiffany and Grant: Tug-of-love

Writer: Simon Ashdown

Transmission date: 31 December 1998

love and death

About the text

Type: Two-hander and group

Characters leave soaps in all sorts of ways. Sometimes to go abroad (as Cindy does in the episode featured earlier in the book), on other occasions running away with a loved one. However, most commonly, they are 'killed off' in a dramatic episode, which comes at the end of a series of storylines that build to a key moment. In this extract, by Simon Ashdown, set on New Year's Eve, Tiffany is planning to leave the Square taking her daughter Courtney with her. However, Grant, Courtney's father, is out of prison, on bail, and confronts Tiffany.

Word level

- How do you imagine Grant says certain words and phrases in conversation with Tiffany on pages 70 and 71? Consider, in particular, 'Nice surprise is it?' and 'Bail. Ever heard of it?'

- Can you find the words that convey Tiffany's feelings in the scene directions? (Note how these words are mainly adjectives but some are nouns and some are verbs.)

Sentence level

- The variety of sentence structures and the use of punctuation provide insights into the way Grant and Tiffany communicate. For example, at one point Tiffany is caught on the defensive and is interrupted as she asks, 'How did you … ?'

- Note how an aggressive dialogue like this features many questions – with the aggressor throwing the questions like darts ('Bout what?', 'Then what?', 'Well are we?'). Who asks most of these questions?

Text level

- The final few frames of the episode feature very little speech. It is worth remembering that although soaps are based around characters and storylines, they are told through the medium of television – a visual medium.

- How does the writer build up the pace and tension as the scene rushes to its conclusion?

Speaking and listening

- What dramatic techniques would the actors playing Tiffany and Grant utilise in the early part of this extract? Think about pace, positioning and tone.

Episode 756
by Simon Ashdown

Tiffany and Grant exchange words in an earlier episode.

Main Characters

Tiffany Mitchell – barmaid at the Queen Vic, Grant Mitchell's wife
Courtney – her daughter

Grant Mitchell – Courtney's father
Phil Mitchell – his brother

Peggy Butcher – Grant and Phil's mother, Frank Butcher's wife

Bianca Butcher – Tiffany's friend

Frank Butcher – Tiffany's father-in-law by marriage

Michael Rose – market inspector

<u>SCENE: 756/38. INT. VIC UPSTAIRS. NIGHT. [11.57pm/</u>
<u>T.C.]</u>

<u>STAGE 1</u>

    [PICK UP TIFFANY COMING TO TOP OF THE STAIRS.

    SHE SEES GRANT AND TIFFANY'S BEDROOM DOOR AJAR,
    LOOKS IN.

    THE BED IS EMPTY, COVER PULLED BACK.

    PUZZLED, SHE STANDS A MOMENT, THEN HEARS A SLIGHT
    NOISE.

    SHE SMILES TO HERSELF, EXITS TO LANDING, HEADS TO
    LOUNGE, ENTERS.

    GRANT, IN A COAT, IS CROUCHED BY SOFA, PUTTING
    COURTNEY'S SHOES ON.

    COURTNEY IS DRESSED IN A COAT AND BOBBLE HAT,
    READY TO GO OUT.

    TIFFANY COMES TO A HALT, STANDS ROOTED TO THE
    SPOT]

<u>GRANT:</u> Hello Tiffany.

    [FOR A MOMENT SHE CAN'T SPEAK.

    SOUNDS FROM DOWNSTAIRS, PREPARATIONS FOR NEW
    YEAR, SLOWLY ESCALATE]

<u>TIFFANY:</u> What are you doing here?

<u>GRANT:</u> Nice surprise is it?

[TIFFANY'S SCARED, TRIES TO APPEAR CALM]

TIFFANY: How did you ... ?

GRANT: Bail. Ever heard of it?

TIFFANY: You shouldn't be here. You ain't meant to be anywhere near me or Courtney.

[COURTNEY STARTS TO GET OFF THE SOFA, MOVE TOWARDS TIFFANY.

GRANT POPS HER BACK ON THE SOFA]

GRANT: You stay there darlin'.

[TIFFANY APPROACHES.

GRANT STEPS FORWARD, BLOCKS HER PATH]

TIFFANY: Just give her to me.

GRANT: I don't think so.

TIFFANY: Grant ...

GRANT: You had me locked up. You were gonna leave me there ...

TIFFANY: That ain't true. I ... I sorted things ...

GRANT: No. You were gonna go off, take my little girl away. Well it ain't gonna happen.

[GRANT PICKS UP BAG.

FAINT SOUND OF COUNTDOWN TO NEW YEAR FROM VIC
DOWNSTAIRS]

TIFFANY: [RISING PANIC] Let's sit down, talk about
it.

GRANT: 'Bout what?

TIFFANY: You and me, everything. I'll tell the police
you didn't do it.

GRANT: Then what? We gonna patch things up? We gonna
give it another go?

    [A BEAT]

Well are we?

    [A MOMENT BETWEEN THEM]

TIFFANY: [EMPTY] No.

GRANT: So, you're still gonna take her?

TIFFANY: Please, Grant, just give her to me ...

GRANT: Why should I? I made one mistake. One stupid,
stupid mistake.

TIFFANY: [CUTS IN] It wasn't one mistake. Just the
last in a long line of things.

GRANT: What things?

TIFFANY: Take your pick. The fact is, you never
really loved me.

GRANT: That's not true.

TIFFANY: You tried, but you never had it in you.

GRANT: That last night ... I said I loved you and I meant it.

TIFFANY: Doesn't matter. It's too late now.

GRANT: Don't you have any feelings for me?

[TIFFANY LOOKS AT GRANT. A LONG MOMENT]

TIFFANY: [UPSET] No. [GENTLE] I'm sorry.

[A BEAT]

Now please, just give her to me.

[GRANT HESITATES, THEN STARTS TO BACK OFF]

GRANT: This ain't happening again. Sharon ran off, left me stranded. You ain't doing it too. You ain't taking Courtney.

[GRANT PICKS UP COURTNEY, STARTS TO MOVE. TIFFANY BLOCKS HIS PATH]

TIFFANY: Please.

GRANT: Get out of my way.

[SOUND OF COURTNEY, BEGINNING TO CRY]

TIFFANY: Grant ...

GRANT: Get out of my way!

    [GRANT TRIES TO MOVE PAST. TIFFANY WON'T LET HIM.

    GRANT PUSHES PAST, HEADS OUT OF THE LOUNGE AND DOWNSTAIRS.

    THE SOUND OF COURTNEY SCREAMING **[OOV]**, MINGLES WITH THE CHEERS, CHIMES OF BIG BEN FROM DOWNSTAIRS]

TIFFANY: [SCREAMS] Grant! Grant, come back here ...

    [TIFFANY FOLLOWS GRANT DOWN THE STAIRS, TRYING TO STOP HIM]

Grant!   CUT TO:

SCENE: 756/39. INT. VIC DOWNSTAIRS. NIGHT. [12.00am/ T.C.]

STAGE 1

    [PICK UP TIFFANY, FOLLOWING GRANT AS HE HEADS DOWNSTAIRS.

    CACOPHONY OF SOUND, CHEERS, SINGING FROM BAR]

TIFFANY: ... she's crying, she wants me ...

    [GRANT IGNORES TIFFANY'S CRIES HEADS TO BAR]

[DESPERATE] Peggy, someone, someone please help me ...

[PEGGY EMERGES INTO BACK AREA, HOLDING CHAMPAGNE GLASS]

PEGGY: [SHOCKED] Grant!

[GRANT BRUSHES PAST, ENTERS BAR]

TIFFANY: He's taking her.

[TIFFANY FOLLOWS GRANT INTO BAR.

PARTY POPPERS, CHEERS, NOISE AND CONFUSION - AS GRANT HEADS PAST PUNTERS]

[PANIC] Somebody stop him.

[PHIL TURNS, IS AMAZED TO SEE GRANT AS HE EXITS INTO STREET]

CUT TO:

SCENE: 756/40 EXT. THE SQUARE/BRIDGE STREET. NIGHT. [12.00am/T.C.]

LOT

[GRANT, CARRYING COURTNEY, BURSTS OUT ONTO FROSTY STREET, SWIFTLY FOLLOWED BY TIFFANY.

GO TO TIFFANY'S **POV** OF GRANT FROM BEHIND - COURTNEY HEARD BUT UNSEEN]

TIFFANY: [HYSTERICAL] Grant you're gonna hurt her. Please, just let her go ... give her back to me. Courtney!

POV point of view

[BIANCA APPEARS AT HER WINDOW, LOOKS DOWN.

BIANCA'S POV OF TIFFANY AND GRANT, TWO FIGURES
IN THE DARKNESS [COURTNEY NOT SEEN] - SOUND OF
TIFFANY PLEADING.

TIFFANY GRABS AT GRANT, THEY SCUFFLE FOR A
MOMENT, PULLING AT EACH OTHER, SLIDING AROUND ON
THE ICY STREET.

SOUND OF COURTNEY, SCREAMING.

GO TO TIFFANY, PULLING AT GRANT'S BACK]

TIFFANY: [PANIC] Give her to me, give her to me ...

[GRANT PUSHES TIFFANY BACK, SHE SLIPS, FALLS
OVER.

PHIL AND PEGGY EXIT FROM VIC, SEE TIFFANY FALL.

TIFFANY'S POV OF GRANT, AS HE HEADS OFF ACROSS
CORNER OF BRIDGE STREET.

GO TO FRANK IN CAR, HEADING DOWN BRIDGE STREET.

PEGGY TURNS BACK TO VIC]

PEGGY: [TO PHIL] I'm calling the police.

PHIL: [STOPS HER] No.

[TIFFANY GETS UP, RUNS AFTER GRANT ACROSS THE
STREET CORNER.

BIANCA ROUNDS CORNER FROM FLAT]

BIANCA: Tiff ...

[GRANT CLUTCHING COURTNEY.

TIFFANY FOLLOWING GRANT, EYES FIXED ON COURTNEY.

MICHAEL IS WALKING IN **B.G.**

FRANK'S CAR COMES OUT OF BRIDGE STREET AND, WITH A SICKENING THUD, RUNS STRAIGHT INTO TIFFANY.

GRANTS STOPS, TURNS.

BIANCA STOPS, HORRIFIED.

PHIL AND PEGGY TURN BACK, STARE AT TIFFANY IN DISBELIEF.

TIFFANY LIES SPRAWLED ON THE STREET, HIT BY FRANK'S CAR.

CAR DOOR OPENS, FRANK EMERGES]

love and death

FRANK: [AGHAST] Oh my Lord.

[BIANCA, DAZED, KNEELS NEXT TO TIFFANY.

TIFFANY TRIES TO MOVE, A STRANGE GUTTURAL NOISE
EMITTING FROM HER THROAT.

SHE TRIES TO LOOK AROUND, HER EYES SEEM UNABLE
TO FIX ON ANYTHING]

PEGGY: [OOV] Call an ambulance someone. Quickly!

[CLOSE ON TIFFANY. SHE LOOKS AT GRANT, THEN
COURTNEY.

TAKE TIFFANY'S POV OF COURTNEY IN GRANT'S ARMS.

A MOMENT ON TIFFANY'S FACE, LOOKING AT COURTNEY,
THEN SHE GENTLY SINKS, INCH BY INCH, BACK ONTO
THE BLOODIED TARMAC]

BIANCA: [HUSHED] Tiff ... [cont]

[TIFFANY'S EYES, OPEN BUT LIFELESS.

BIANCA, STUNNED, LOOKS UP AT GRANT]

BIANCA: [cont] [TEARFUL DISBELIEF] She's dead.

[GRANT STANDS, PARALYSED WITH SHOCK, HOLDING
COURTNEY.

OUT ON TIFFANY, SPRAWLED AWKWARDLY ON THE FROSTY
STREET]

FADE OUT

Kat and Zoe:
Mother and Child

Writer: Tony Jordan

Transmission date: 2 October 2001

About the text

Type: Two-hander

There are two extracts here, from the start of the episode and from the end. The first deals with the news given by Kat at the end of the previous episode – that Zoe, her 'younger sister', is in fact her daughter. The second reveals an equally startling piece of information at the end. This is a good example of a key episode ending with a 'bang'. This episode, written by Tony Jordan, is also unusual in that it features two characters only. This gives the writer the opportunity for longer, more reflective speeches – although these can be as emotionally charged as shorter dialogues.

Word level

- How does 'Best not' – a simple phrase ('It's best not to') – take on emotional meaning when it is used on pages 90 and 91? Do you agree with the advice?

- Consider the variety of verbs used in the scene directions to describe Zoe and Kat's behaviour and feelings (for example, 'SHE STEELS HERSELF', 'SHE SPINS ON HEELS...' etc.).

Sentence level

- Notice how the writer uses ellipses dots (...), especially in the longer speeches, to hint at how the speech should be delivered, and where pauses might come. When a longer pause is required, the word 'BEAT' is used.

- Consider the impact of the very short sentences, or even single words, in several of Kat's speeches. Look at where she says 'Clean' on page 90. What does she mean? Why is this so effective?

- How does the writer use repetition in Kat's speech on page 91 to convey her feelings?

Text level

- At the end of the episode Kat does not come out with the truth straight away. How is it revealed in several lines of speech and through Kat's actions?

- Throughout the exchanges between Kat and Zoe, Kat talks about moments from her past. Can you find examples of when she does this? How does this add emotional power to the drama?

Episode 34
by Tony Jordan

Main Characters

Kat Slater

One of the Slater sisters. Kat is seen as the lazy and rebellious member of the Slater family. With a tough exterior and a big mouth, it seems that Kat is the real hard nut of the family. It is only in this episode that we begin to see her vulnerable side and the possible reason for her wild behaviour.

Zoe Slater

Her daughter. Zoe Slater is the baby of the Slater family. In the days that ran up to this momentous night, things appeared to be going right for Zoe. Although she was messed around by Jamie Mitchell and had just lost her job on Mark Fowler's fruit and veg stall, she jumped at the chance to go to Spain with her Uncle Harry. She could hardly have expected the reaction she got from her 'sister' Kat, when she announced her decision at Lynne's hen night.

DIRECT PICK UP FROM PREVIOUS EPISODE;

SCENE 34/1. BRIDGE STREET. EXT. NIGHT. [11.30pm]

LOT

OPENING TITLE MUSIC

> [BOISTEROUS NOISE COMING FROM INSIDE QUEEN VIC;
>
> ZOE STARES AT KAT]

ZOE: What did you say?

> [A MOMENT BETWEEN THEM, KAT'S MIND RACES, SHOULD SHE CONTINUE CONVERSATION, OR NOT ... ?
>
> EVENTUALLY SHE **BOTTLES IT** AND STRIDES PAST ZOE ON HER WAY HOME]

KAT: [AS SHE PASSES ZOE] Nothing, it don't matter.

> [A BEAT, ZOE BEMUSED, NOT SURE WHAT TO DO.
>
> SHE EVENTUALLY ELECTS TO GO AFTER KAT, CATCHING HER UP IN GARDENS]

ZOE: [RUNNING AFTER HER] I want to know what you meant.

KAT: [OVER HER SHOULDER] No you don't Zo.

ZOE: Where are you going?

KAT: Home. Just go back to the party.

ZOE: Not until you've told me why you said that.

[AS KAT NEARS SLATER'S HOUSE SHE TAKES OUT KEYS]

Kat ... Kat! Kat, wait.

[BUT KAT OPENS DOOR AND GOES INSIDE, ZOE FOLLOWS
NOT FAR BEHIND]

CUT TO:

SCENE 34/2. SLATERS' KITCHEN. INT. NIGHT. [11.33pm]

STAGE 1

[PICK UP KAT AS SHE ENTERS, ZOE CLOSE BEHIND HER]

ZOE: Well?

KAT: [MOCK INNOCENCE] Well what?

ZOE: You can't just say something like that and just
run off.

[A BEAT]

KAT: Let's not do this eh, Zo?

ZOE: Do what exactly?

[KAT MOVES AWAY, SHE'S MANIC, AVOIDING EYE
CONTACT, TRAPPED, HAS NO IDEA HOW OR WHETHER TO
DO THIS. SHE HEADS FOR A KITCHEN CUPBOARD AND
TAKES OUT A GLASS AND A BOTTLE OF WHISKY]

KAT: [LAUGHS] Look, I was joking, where's your sense
of humour?

ZOE: I don't believe you.

KAT: You shouldn't take things so seriously ...

ZOE: No. That weren't a joke ... You were angry.

KAT: Look, why don't we go back to the party, yeah?
And we could tell Belinda about when we went to
Brighton and trashed that bloke's flat ...

ZOE: [CUTS IN] You said you were my mother.

    [A MOMENT BETWEEN THEM.

    KATS SITS - HYSTERICAL LAUGHTER]

KAT: So I did.

    [A LONG MOMENT - KAT STARES AT TABLE]

ZOE: Please ...

KAT: Leave it, Zo. It doesn't matter.

ZOE: It matters to me.

    [A BEAT]

Is it true? [cont]

    [A BEAT - KAT JUST CAN'T SAY THE WORDS;

    ZOE SWIPES KAT'S GLASS OFF THE TABLE WITH HER
ARM, IT CRASHES TO THE FLOOR]

ZOE: [cont] Finish what you were saying!

KAT: I can't.

ZOE: Why not?

KAT: I don't know where to start.

ZOE: How about the bit where you said you were my mum?

> [KAT CORNERED, NOT WANTING TO BE THERE, HAVING THIS CONVERSATION]

Kat please ... [A BEAT] Just tell me the truth.

> [KAT OPENS HER MOUTH TO SPEAK BUT NOTHING COMES OUT.
>
> INSTEAD, SHE WAILS, THEN STARTS TO SOB.
>
> PITIFUL, SHE DOESN'T WANT THIS]

Tell me! [cont]

> [KAT CONTINUES TO SOB]

Is it true? [A BEAT] Are you my mum?

> [KAT STILL CAN'T FIND THE WORDS — SHE STEELS HERSELF, THEN NODS;
>
> TAKE ZOE'S REACTION; GENUINE SHOCK AS IT'S MADE REAL BY KAT'S ADMISSION.
>
> SHE STARES AT KAT.
>
> A MOMENT BETWEEN THEM, FEELS LIKE AN ETERNITY FOR BOTH.
>
> BOTH WAITING FOR THE OTHER TO REACT.
>
> IT'S ZOE FIRST]

You're a liar!

* This scene is taken from later in the same episode.

[SHE SPINS ON HEELS AND WALKS OUT.

KAT IS ON HER FEET IMMEDIATELY]

KAT: Zoe ...

[BUT ZOE'S GONE]

SCENE 34/27*. SLATERS' LIVING ROOM. INT. NIGHT.
[11.40pm]

STAGE 1

Music: "Hello" - Oasis

[ZOE CURLED UP INTO A BALL ON SOFA.

MUSIC BLARING.

KAT ENTERS, TURNS OFF STEREO.

SLOWLY WALKS AND SITS ON ARM OF SOFA]

KAT: What I said in there was true. But it wasn't always like that, and if you don't believe anything else, you have to believe that. [A BEAT] I remember the day it changed ... I was lying in the bath. And you moved. I saw something poke out like an elbow or something, just for a second, then it disappeared. From that second you stopped being a thing ... and you was my baby. And from that second to this, I've loved you more than anything else in this world.

[ZOE LOOKS AT HER FOR THE FIRST TIME]

I even went and asked Mum if I could keep you. She said that everyone'd worked so hard to sort things out that I wasn't to ruin anything. [A BEAT] She said I could pick your name, but that was to be an end to it.

ZOE: So you gave up?

KAT: [A BEAT] I never gave up. They took you away from me and I didn't know how to stop 'em. [A BEAT] But at least I knew that I'd see you every day, and love you... . If not as a Mum then as a sister.

    [KAT LAUGHS AND STANDS, PACING ROOM]

Shows you what an idiot I am ... . It's turned into a nightmare. I had to listen to everyone telling Mum how lucky she was to have such a beautiful baby ... And all the time I wanted to scream at them that you were mine ... And it was me they should be talking to ...

    [KAT SITS ON SOFA BESIDE ZOE]

But I couldn't, so more often than not I had to leave the room. Everyone called me a stroppy cow and ignored me. [A BEAT] Back on the stairs again.

ZOE: What about when I was older? Why didn't you tell me then?

KAT: How would it have helped for you to know?

ZOE: At least I would have known who I am!

    [A MOMENT]

KAT: But you're still the same person. Nothing changes that.

ZOE: I thought my mum was dead!

KAT: I know ...

ZOE: Why didn't you tell me then? When she died?

KAT: I thought about it. But Dad said you was still too young.

ZOE: So instead you waited a couple of years and spit it at me in the middle of the street.

KAT: I know, I didn't mean that to happen.

ZOE: Because I was doing something you didn't agree with.

KAT: Partly to do with that, yeah.

ZOE: Bit late to be playing mummies innit?

KAT: [STARES AT ZOE] I've always been your mum, whether you knew it or not.

[A MOMENT BETWEEN THEM.

ZOE SEES KAT'S CUT LIP]

ZOE: You're bleeding.

KAT: Oh, it don't matter.

[ZOE TAKES OUT HANDKERCHIEF]

ZOE: Yes it does, come here ...

[ZOE DABS KAT'S BLOODIED LIP]

KAT: I've made a real mess of it, ain't I?

ZOE: Pretty much.

KAT: I still feel better now that you know.

ZOE: Wish I did.

KAT: You might do one day.

[A BEAT]

ZOE: Who else knows?

KAT: Dad, Lynne ... . Nan. Belinda and Little Mo were too young.

[A BEAT]

ZOE: I can't believe you're my mum. [A BEAT] I weren't that keen on you as a sister ...

KAT: Can't blame you for that.

ZOE: You were always so bossy.

KAT: Now you know why.

[A BEAT]

We can get over this Zo, I know we can.

ZOE: Can we?

KAT: If you want to.

ZOE: I don't know what I want.

[A MOMENT]

Can I ask you something?

KAT: Yeah, course you can ...

ZOE: What happened when I was born? Did you keep me for a little while?

KAT: Well, they took me to the hospital, Mum said I was to have a room on my own ... 'cause I'd be more comfortable, but I knew it was because she was ashamed. [A BEAT] The birth was like a dream, like it was happening to someone else, and I was just watching.
[A BEAT] Afterwards ... Mum went out to phone Dad and the nurses came in and they wrapped you in this blue sheet thing and they gave you to me to hold. I started crying. Soppy cow.

ZOE: That ugly was I?

KAT: You were the most beautiful thing I've ever seen. They wrapped you up so tightly, all I could see was your little face looking up at me with the biggest bluest eyes, and a little tuft of jet black hair poking out the top. You were perfect. [A BEAT] I'd never been proud of anything before, but I was then ... I wanted the whole world to see you, to show 'em what I'd done ... Tell 'em you were mine ... My little girl. And I felt perfect an' all. Clean. [A BEAT] And then Mum come in and took you off me. She started walking 'round the room with you ... Telling you all the things she was gonna do for you, how she was gonna look after you ... All the things I should have been saying. [A BEAT] And then Dad come in and I felt dirty again. He hardly looked at me. I had to lay there watching 'em fussing over you and all the time I wanted to scream at 'em, to give you back ... But I couldn't, 'cause Dad would give me that look again, to say how disappointed he was with me ... And why wasn't I like the others ... So I didn't. When he left, I asked Mum if I could hold you ... D'you know what she said? "Best not" [A BEAT] "Best not" [A BEAT] If only I could have held you ... just for a few more minutes ...

[ZOE STUDIES KAT - FEELING HER PAIN. SHE SLOWLY
LEANS FORWARD TO REST HER HEAD ON KAT'S SHOULDER.

KAT GENTLY STROKES HER HAIR.

MOTHER AND DAUGHTER]

KAT: Things were never the same after that. Birthdays,
Christmas ... first day at school ... always in the
background, always with that same anger I had the day
you were born ... Always wanting to say something ...
But best not. [A BEAT] I remember sometimes, you'd
come in from school, upset over something and you'd
run straight past me to Mum ...

ZOE: I'm sorry.

KAT: It wasn't your fault. [A BEAT] I used to nick you
sometimes though ...

ZOE: What?

KAT: I used to take you to the park ... Just you and
me. It was brilliant. [A BEAT] I remember one day,
you couldn't have been more than three, we was making
daisy chains and you wanted to play a game where I
pretended to be the mum ... You even called me Mummy.
I don't think I've ever been that happy.

ZOE: I'm sorry I hit you.

KAT: It doesn't matter.

ZOE: What d'you think Dad'll say. When he finds out I
know?

KAT: I dunno.

ZOE: You and him are alright now though aren't you?

KAT: Yeah ... It's been better since Mum died.

ZOE: He always says you remind him of her.

KAT: Yeah ...

ZOE: You did make up though ... After I was born?

KAT: We stayed out of each other's way really. I went a bit wild. After he found out I was pregnant he just put me down as a slapper ... . Didn't want to disappoint him again did I?

        [ZOE HAS A THOUGHT - SITS BOLT UPRIGHT]

What?

ZOE: You ain't told me who my dad is.

KAT: What?

ZOE: My dad.

KAT: [PANIC] Don't worry about him ...

ZOE: What do you mean "don't worry about him" ... ? I want to know who he is.

KAT: He didn't even know I was pregnant.

ZOE: What was his name?

KAT: I can't remember.

ZOE: You "can't remember"?

KAT: It was a long time ago.

ZOE: I don't believe you got pregnant and don't even know who the dad was. [SUDDENLY REMEMBERING] You said he was older.

KAT: I didn't say I didn't know who he was. I said I couldn't remember his name ... [STANDS] Look, I fancy a drink, d'you want one?

[KAT RETREATS TO KITCHEN]

CUT TO:

SCENE 34/28. SLATERS' KITCHEN. INT. NIGHT. [11.45pm]

STAGE 1

[KAT ENTERS KITCHEN AND POURS HERSELF A DRINK.

ZOE ENTERS AND STANDS IN DOORWAY]

ZOE: Would you help me find him? My Dad?

KAT: One day.

ZOE: Promise.

[KAT AND ZOE SIT AT THE TABLE]

[A BEAT] I mean I don't know if I wanna speak to him or anything, but I'd like to know who he is.

KAT: One thing at a time, yeah?

ZOE: Yeah ...

[A BEAT]

So what happens now?

KAT: That's up to you.

[A BEAT]

ZOE: I need time to think.

KAT: 'Course you do.

ZOE: It's probably a good job I'm going away, be easier to get my head together.

KAT: What?

ZOE: In Spain.

KAT: You can't go Zo ...

ZOE: But there's even more reason for me to go now ... I'll have time to myself, to work things out.

KAT: No.

ZOE: Why not?

KAT: You just can't.

ZOE: But it's perfect.

KAT: No it isn't.

ZOE: I'll be safe, Harry's gonna look after me.

KAT: [ANGRILY] Look, you're not going to Spain and that's the end of it. Drop it.

ZOE: Why are you being like this?

    [KAT IGNORES HER]

This ain't up to you. You can't start being a mum and laying down the law just like that. If Dad says it's alright, what's the problem?

KAT: Dad don't understand.

ZOE: Understand what?

KAT: Nothing. You're just not going and that's that!

ZOE: I'm old enough to do what I want and you ain't gonna stop me.

KAT: Zoe ... Zoe ...

    [ZOE WALKS OUT OF THE KITCHEN, KAT RUNS AFTER HER, CATCHING HER AT THE BOTTOM OF THE STAIRS]

Zoe!

    [KAT GRABS HER ARM]

ZOE: Get off me! What is the matter with you?

KAT: You're not going, not with him!

ZOE: With who?

    [ZOE STUDIES KAT, SHE SEES SHE'S DISTRAUGHT, FIGHTING BACK TEARS ...]

Uncle Harry? [cont]

    [A BEAT - KAT LOSING IT]

ZOE: [cont] Kat? [A BEAT] Tell me!

KAT: [CRYING NOW, BLURTS OUT] It wasn't my fault.

ZOE: What weren't?

KAT: He told me I was his special girl.

ZOE: Who?

KAT: Dad kept asking me, "Who is it?", his face ... he hated me. He kept on ... "Who is it?" What he was gonna do to him. I wanted to tell him, I wanted to tell him so badly ... but I couldn't ...

ZOE: Why?

KAT: Because it was his brother! It was Harry.

[TAKE ZOE'S REACTION - NOT FULLY UNDERSTANDING]

FADE OUT

CLOSING TITLE MUSIC